Published in the UK by
POWERFRESH Limited
3 Gray Street
Northampton
NN1 3QQ

Telephone   01604 630 996
Facsimile   01604 621 013
E Mail   pwrfresh@nccnet.co.uk

C000216858

Copyright © 1998 SILVEY-JEX PARTNERSHIP

Cover and interior layout by Powerfresh

ISBN 1 874125 75 9

All rights reserved. No part of this publication may be
reproduced or transmitted in any form or by any means,
electronic or mechanical,including photocopying, recording
or any information storage and retrieval system, or for the
source of ideas without the written permission of the publisher.

Printed in the UK by Avalon Print Northampton
Powerfresh June 1998

THE SILVEY-JEX PARTNERSHIP

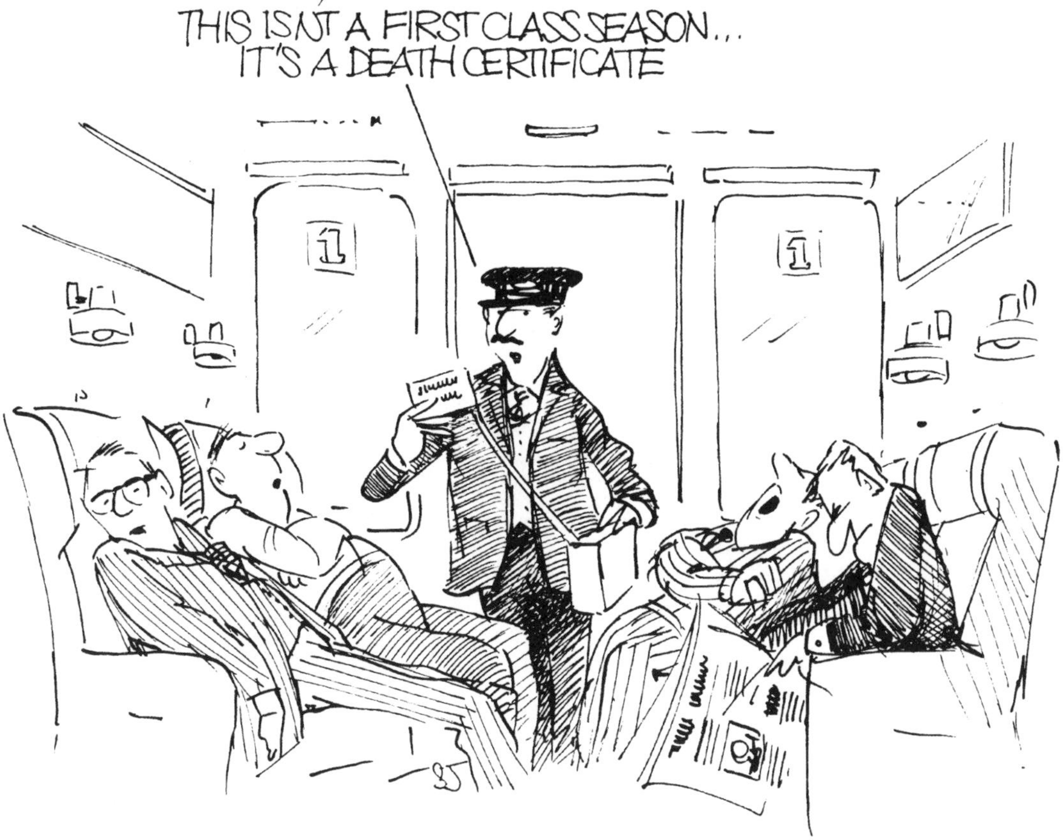
THIS ISN'T A FIRST CLASS SEASON...
IT'S A DEATH CERTIFICATE

I'D BETTER GO MOTHER — GEORGE HAS JUST DIED

HELLO DOCTOR... WHAT CAN YOU TELL ME ABOUT RIGOR MORTIS?

FUNERAL
DIRECTORS

WHAT SHALL WE SAY.... A DEAD HEAT?

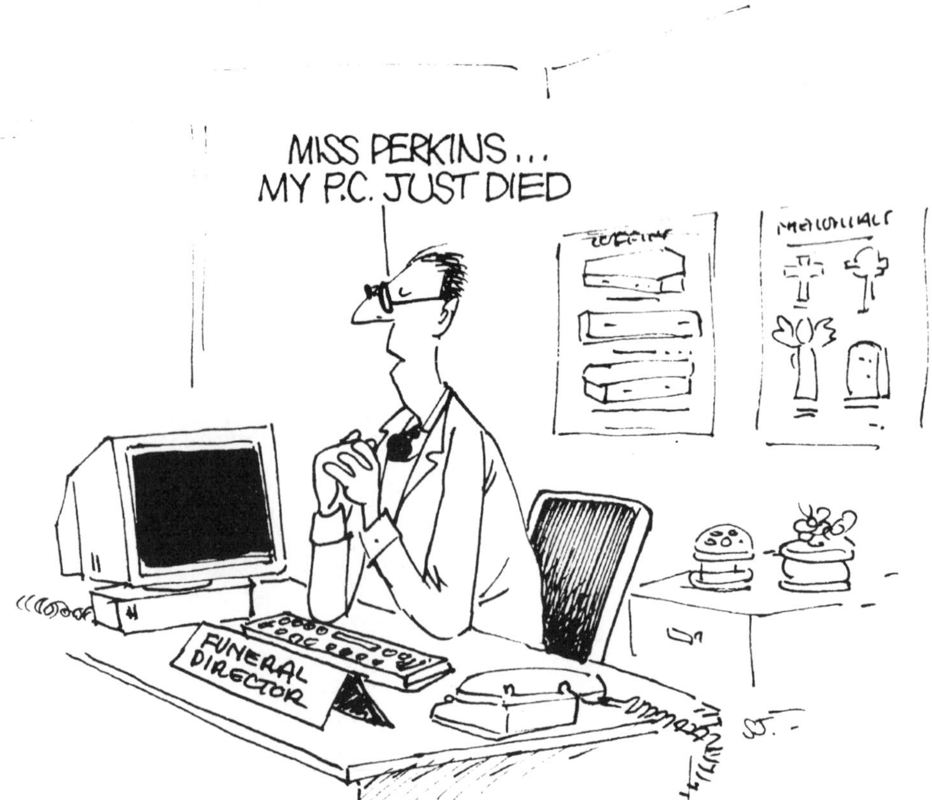
MISS PERKINS...
MY P.C. JUST DIED
FUNERAL DIRECTOR

I WAS VERY SCEPTICAL ABOUT LEVITATION UNTIL NOW

WHAT?...LEAVE EARLY? OVER MY DEAD BODY

YES...THAT'S HIM.

POOR GRANDAD DIED PEACEFULLY IN THE BATH
AND WE DIDN'T HAVE THE HEART TO MOVE HIM

MUM! SOMETHING'S BURNING!!

THE "SAW THE LADY IN HALF" TRICK THAT WENT HORRIBLY WRONG

YOUR GRANDAD ALWAYS ENJOYED BONFIRE NIGHT DIDN'T HE?

SHOW A LITTLE RESPECT MAN!!

WELL HE WAS A VERY <u>BIG</u> MAN YOUR HUSBAND

AAH...JUST LOOK AT HIM...THAT WEEK IN BLACKPOOL DID HIM THE POWER OF GOOD

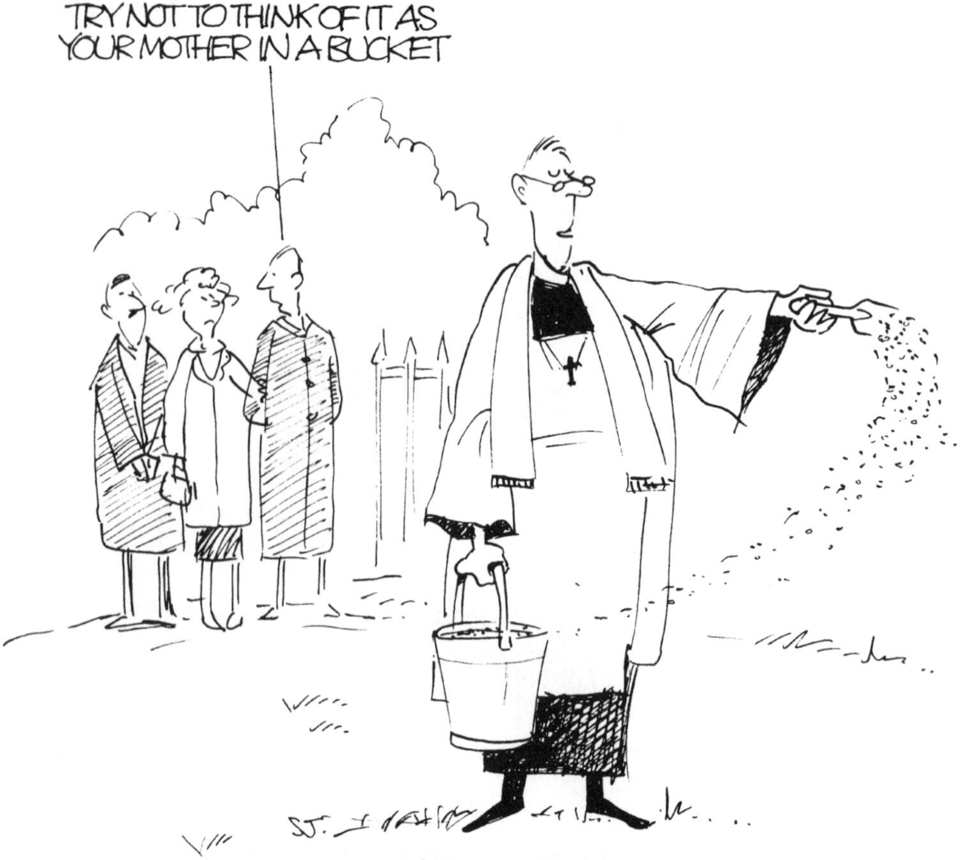
TRY NOT TO THINK OF IT AS YOUR MOTHER IN A BUCKET

ER, EXCUSE ME, HAS ANYBODY GOT A LIGHT?

SO YOU'VE SEEN YOUR EX-WIFE... I SEE MY EX-HUSBAND ALL THE TIME

IS ANYBODY THERE?

HE'LL KILL HIMSELF ONE OF THESE DAYS

HE NEVER TOOK HIS RELIGION SERIOUSLY—SO IT SERVES HIM RIGHT

WELL...IT'S JUST THAT I IMAGINED YOU SORT OF BIGGER SOMEHOW

IF I'D HAVE KNOWN IT WAS LIKE THIS I'D HAVE COME SOONER

THE ANGEL OF DEAF

CRINKLED 'N' WRINKLED	PMT CRAZED
DRIVEN CRAZY	HORNY MAN'S ADULT DOODLE BOOK
TRUE LOVE	HORNY GIRL'S ADULT DOODLE BOOK
IT'S A BOY	IF BABIES COULD TALK
IT'S A GIRL	CAT CRAZY
OH NO IT'S XMAS AGAIN	MAD TO TRAVEL BY AIR...
FUNNY SIDE OF 30s	MAD TO PLAY GOLF...
FUNNY SIDE OF 40 HIM	MAD TO HAVE A BABY...
FUNNY SIDE OF 40 HER	MAD TO GET MARRIED...
FUNNY SIDE OF 50 HIM	MAD TO HAVE A PONY
FUNNY SIDE OF 50 HER	MAD TO HAVE A CAT
FUNNY SIDE OF 60'S	MAD TO HAVE A COMPUTER
FUNNY SIDE OF SEX	YOU DON'T HAVE TO BE MAD TO BE 40 HIM
FLYING FUNNIES	YOU DON'T HAVE TO BE MAD TO BE 40 HER
GOLFAHOLICS	YOU DON'T HAVE TO BE MAD TO BE 50 HIM
CHUNKY "N HUNKY	YOU DON'T HAVE TO BE MAD TO BE 50 HER
FOOTNOTES	MAD ON FOOTBALL
MIDLIFE CRISIS	MAD TO BE A MOTHER
WE'RE GETTING MARRIED	MAD TO BE A FATHER
THE DEFINITIVE GUIDE TO VASECTOMY	THE BARE BOTTOM BOOK
KEEP FIT WITH YOUR CAT	GOOD WHILE IT LASTED
MARITAL BLISS AND OTHER OXYMORONS	FUNNY FARM SILLY MOOS
THE OFFICE FROM HELL	

For more information on these or other titles please write to :
Powerfresh Ltd. 3 Gray Street, Northampton, NN1 3QQ, ENGLAND.
Telephone 01604 630 996 Fax 01604 621 013
E Mail pwrfresh@ nccnet.co.uk